FREE STUFF FOR KIDS

Our Pledge

We have collected and examined the best free and up-to-a-dollar offers we could find. Each supplier in this book has promised to honor properly made requests for **single items** through **1995**. Though mistakes do happen, we are doing our best to make sure this book really works.

Meadowbrook Press
Distributed by Simon & Schuster
New York

The Free Stuff Editors

Director: Bruce Lansky
Editor/Researcher: Craig Hansen
Managing Editor: Dale Howard
Editorial Coordinator: Cathy Broberg
Production Manager: Amy Unger
Desktop/Prepress Manager: Patrick Gross
Designer: Erik Broberg

ISBN: 0-88166-212-7
Simon & Schuster Ordering #: 0-671-8998-05

ISSN: 1056-9693
18th edition

Published by Meadowbrook Press, 18318 Minnetonka Boulevard, Deephaven, MN 55391.

BOOK TRADE DISTRIBUTION by Simon & Schuster, a division of Simon and Schuster, Inc., 1230 Avenue of the Americas, New York, NY 10020.

95 94   5 4 3 2 1

Printed in the United States of America

Contents

Thank You's

To Pat Blakely, Barbara Haislet, and Judith Hentges for creating and publishing the original *Rainbow Book*, proving that kids, parents, and teachers would respond enthusiastically to a source of free things by mail. They taught us the importance of carefully checking the quality of each item and doing our best to make sure that each and every request is satisfied.

Our heartfelt appreciation goes to hundreds of organizations and individuals for making this book possible. The suppliers and editors of this book have a common goal: to make it possible for kids to reach out and discover the world by themselves.

READ THIS FIRST

About This Book

Free Stuff for Kids lists hundreds of items you can send away for. The Free Stuff Editors have examined every item and think each is among the best offers available. There are no trick offers—only safe, fun, and informative things you'll like!

This book is designed for kids who can read and write. The directions in **Read This First** explain exactly how to request an item. Read the instructions carefully so you know how to send a request. Making sure you've filled out a request correctly is easy—just complete the *Free Stuff for Kids* Checklist on page 8. Half the fun is using the book on your own. The other half is getting a real reward for your efforts!

Each year the Free Stuff Editors create a new edition of this book, taking out old items, inserting new ones, and changing addresses and prices. It is important for you to use an updated edition because the suppliers only honor properly made requests for single items for the **current** edition. If you use this edition after **1995,** your request might not be honored.

Getting Your Book in Shape

Before sending for free stuff, get your book in shape. Fold it open one page at a time, working from the two ends toward the middle. This will make the book lie flat when you read or copy addresses.

Reading Carefully

Read the descriptions of the offers carefully to find out exactly what you're getting. Here are some guidelines to help you know what you're sending for:

• A pamphlet or foldout is usually one sheet of paper folded over and printed on both sides.
• A booklet is usually larger and contains more pages, but it's smaller than a book.

Following Directions

It's important to follow each supplier's directions. On one offer, you might need to use a postcard. On another offer, you might be asked to include money or a long self-addressed, stamped envelope. If you do not follow the directions **exactly,** you might not get your request. Ask for only **one** of anything you send for. Family or classroom members using the same book must send separate requests.

Sending Postcards

A postcard is a small card you can write on and send through the mail without an envelope. Many suppliers offering free items require you to send requests on postcards. Please do this. It saves them the time it takes to open many envelopes.

The post office sells postcards with pre-printed postage. You can also buy postcards at a drugstore and put special postcard stamps on them yourself. Your local post office can tell you how much a postcard stamp currently costs. (Postcards with a picture on them are usually more expensive.) You must use a postcard that is at least 3½ by 5½ inches. (The post office will not take 3-by-5-inch index cards.) Your postcards should be addressed like the one below.

Amy Lyons
110 Deerwood
Conroe, TX 77303

The Chicago Bulls
Fan Mail
1901 West Madison
Chicago, IL 60612

Dear Sir or Madam:

Please send me a Chicago Bulls fan pack. Thank you very much.

Sincerely,
Amy Lyons
110 Deerwood
Conroe, TX 77303

- **Neatly print** the supplier's address on the side of the postcard that has the postage. Put your return address in the upper left-hand corner of that side as well.
- **Neatly print** your request, your name, and your address on the blank side of the postcard.
- Do not abbreviate the name of your street or city.
- Use a ballpoint pen.

Sending Letters

Your letters should look like the one below.

- **Neatly print** the name of the item you want exactly as you see it in the directions.
- **Neatly print** your own name and address at the bottom of the letter. (Do not abbreviate the name of your street or city.)
- If you're including coins or a long self-addressed, stamped envelope, say so in the letter.
- Put a **first-class stamp** on any envelope you send. You can get stamps at the post office.
- **Neatly print** the supplier's address in the center of the envelope and your return address in the upper left-hand corner.
- If you're sending many letters at once, make sure you put the right letter in the right envelope.
- Use a ballpoint pen. Pencil can be difficult to read, and ink pen often smears.

Sending a Long Self-Addressed, Stamped Envelope

If the directions say to enclose a long self-addressed, stamped envelope, here's how to do it:

- **Neatly print** your name and address in the center of a **9½-inch-long envelope** as if you were mailing it to yourself. Print your return address in the upper left-hand corner of the envelope as well. Put a first-class stamp on it.
- **Fold up** (but don't seal!) the long self-addressed, stamped envelope, and put it inside another **9½-inch-long envelope** (along with your letter to the supplier) and put a **first-class stamp** on it.
- **Neatly print** the supplier's address in the center of the envelope you are sending and your return address in the upper left-hand corner.
- Use a ballpoint pen.

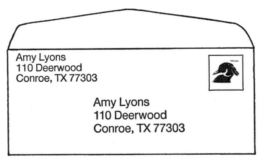

Amy Lyons
110 Deerwood
Conroe, TX 77303

Amy Lyons
110 Deerwood
Conroe, TX 77303

Sending Money

Many of the suppliers in this book are not charging you for their items. However, the cost of postage and handling is high today, and suppliers must charge you for this. If the directions say to enclose money for postage and handling, you must do so. Here are a few rules about sending money:

- Tape the coins to your letter so they won't break out of the envelope.
- Don't stack your coins on top of each other in the envelope.
- If an item costs $1.00, send a one-dollar bill instead of coins. Don't tape dollar bills.
- Send only U.S. money.
- If a grown-up is helping you, he/she may write a check.
- Send all money directly to the suppliers—their addresses are listed with their offers.

Getting Your Free Stuff

Expect to wait **four to eight weeks** for your free stuff to arrive. Sometimes you have to wait longer. Remember, suppliers get thousands of requests each year. Please be patient! If you wait a long time and your offer still doesn't come, you may be using the wrong edition. This is the **1995** edition—the offers in this book will only be good for 1994 and 1995!

Making Sure You Get Your Request

The Free Stuff Editors have tried to make the directions for using this book as clear as possible to make sure you get what you send for. But you must follow **all** of the directions **exactly** as they're written, or the supplier will not be able to answer your request. If you're confused about the directions, ask a grown-up to help you.

Do's and Don'ts:

- **Do** use a ballpoint pen.
- **Do** print. Cursive can be difficult to read.
- **Do** print your name, address, and zip code clearly and fully on the postcard or on the envelope **and** the letter you send. Do not abbreviate anything except state names. Abbreviations can be confusing, and sometimes envelopes and letters get separated after they reach the supplier.
- **Do** send the correct amount of U.S. money, but use as few coins as possible.
- **Do** tape the coins you send to the letter you send them with. If you don't, the money might rip the envelope and fall out.
- **Do** use a **9½-inch-long** self-addressed, stamped envelope if the instructions say you should.

- **Do not** ask for more than **one** of an item.
- **Do not** stack coins in the envelope.
- **Do not** seal your long self-addressed, stamped envelope. The suppliers need to be able to put the item you ordered in the envelope you send.
- **Do not** ask Meadowbrook Press to send you any of the items listed in the book unless you are ordering the Meadowbrook offers from p. 44 or p. 47. The publishers of this book do not carry items belonging to other suppliers. They do not supply refunds, either.

Follow all the rules to avoid disappointment!

What to Do If You Aren't Satisfied:

If you have complaints about any offer, or if you don't receive the items you sent for within eight to ten weeks, contact the Free Stuff Editors. Before you complain, please reread the directions. Are you sure you followed them properly? Are you using this **1995** edition **after** 1995? (Offers here are only good for 1994 and 1995.) The Free Stuff Editors won't be able to send you the item, but they can make sure that any suppliers who don't fulfill requests are dropped from next year's *Free Stuff for Kids*. We'd like to know which offers you like and what kind of new offers you'd like us to add to next year's edition. So don't be bashful—write us a letter. Send your complaints or suggestions to:

The Free Stuff Editors
Meadowbrook Press
18318 Minnetonka Boulevard
Deephaven, MN 55391

Free Stuff for Kids Checklist

Use this checklist each time you send out a request. It will help you follow directions **exactly** and prevent mistakes. Put a check mark in the box each time you complete a task—you can photocopy this page and use it again and again.

When sending postcards and letters:
❑ I used a ballpoint pen.

❑ I printed neatly and carefully.

❑ I asked for the correct item (only one).

❑ I wrote to the correct supplier.

❑ I double-checked the supplier's address.

When sending postcards only:
❑ I put my return address on the postcard.

❑ I applied a postcard stamp (if the postage wasn't pre-printed).

When sending letters only:
❑ I put my return address on the letter.

❑ I included a **9½-inch** self-addressed, stamped envelope (if the directions asked for one).

❑ I included the correct amount of money (if the directions asked for money).

❑ I put my return address on the envelope.

❑ I applied a **first-class stamp.**

When sending a long self-addressed, stamped envelope:
❑ I used a **9½-inch-long** envelope.

❑ I put my address on the front of the envelope.

❑ I put my return address in the upper left-hand corner of the envelope.

❑ I left the envelope unsealed.

❑ I applied a **first-class stamp.**

When sending a one-dollar bill:
❑ I sent U.S. money.

❑ I enclosed a one-dollar bill with my letter instead of coins.

When sending coins:
❑ I sent U.S. money.

❑ I taped the coins to my letter.

❑ I did not stack the coins on top of each other.

SPORTS

Minnesota Twins

The Minnesota Twins have a can't-miss offer. Send for a schedule, brochure, and photo packet (depending on availability) from the team that features two-time World Series hero Kirby Puckett.

Directions:	Write your request on paper, and put it in an envelope. You must enclose a **long self-addressed, stamped envelope.**
Write to:	Fan Mail Minnesota Twins 501 Chicago Avenue South Minneapolis, MN 55415
Ask for:	Minnesota Twins pocket schedule, novelty brochure, and team/player photos

Texas Rangers

Cheer on the Texas Rangers with this fan pack which includes a team schedule, logo sticker, and souvenir list (depending on availability).

Directions:	Write your request on paper, and put it in an envelope. You must enclose a **long self-addressed, stamped envelope.**
Write to:	Texas Rangers Souvenirs P.O. Box 90111 Arlington, TX 76004-3111
Ask for:	Texas Rangers schedule, sticker, and souvenir list

New York Yankees

One of the American League's oldest and most celebrated teams has an offer that's a home run. Send for a New York Yankees bumper sticker, schedule, and decal (depending on availability).

Directions:	Write your request on paper, and put it in an envelope. You must enclose a **long self-addressed, stamped envelope.**
Write to:	Community Relations Department c/o Yankees Fan Pack New York Yankees Yankees Stadium Bronx, NY 10451
Ask for:	New York Yankees bumper sticker, pocket schedule, and decal

Boston Red Sox

Here's a great catch! This Red Sox fan pack includes a brochure, pocket schedule, and player postcard (depending on availability). You'll also get information on how you can join the Coca-Cola Rookie Red Sox fan club and the Fenway Park tours.

Directions:	Write your request on paper, and put it in an envelope. You must enclose an **8-by-10-inch self-addressed, stamped envelope.**
Write to:	Red Sox Fan Stuff 4 Yawkey Way Boston, MA 02215
Ask for:	Boston Red Sox brochure, pocket schedule, player postcard, and fan information

Philadelphia Phillies

Here's a great offer from the 1993 National League champs! Their fan pack includes a pocket schedule, team logo sticker, and two player photocards (depending on availability). Fans of the team's mascot can ask for a Phillie Phanatic decal and photocard.

Directions:	Write your request on paper, and put it in an envelope. You must enclose a **long self-addressed, stamped envelope.**
Write to:	Phillies Fan Mail P.O. Box 7575 Philadelphia, PA 19101
Ask for:	• Philadelphia Phillies pocket schedule, logo sticker, and two player photocards • Phillie Phanatic sticker and photocard

Houston Astros

Did you know the Houston Astros were the first team to use a domed stadium and artificial turf? Their fan pack features a schedule, logo sticker, and player photo (depending on availability).

Directions:	Write your request on paper, and put it in an envelope. You must enclose a **long self-addressed, stamped envelope.**
Write to:	Houston Astros Public Relations P.O. Box 288 Houston, TX 77001-0288
Ask for:	Houston Astros schedule, logo sticker, and player photo

Team Stickers

Support your favorite teams with these baseball team sticker packs. Each sticker pack features eight colorful stickers. Choose any major league team—including the new Colorado Rockies and Florida Marlins! (Please specify which baseball team you want.)

Directions:	Write your request on paper, and put it in an envelope. You must enclose **$1.25.** (We think this offer is a good value for the money.)
Write to:	Mr. Rainbows Department K-14 P.O. Box 908 Rio Grande, NJ 08242
Ask for:	Baseball team sticker pack (specify the team you want)

Chicago Bulls

Support the Scottie Pippen–led Chicago Bulls as they stampede toward another NBA title. This world-class fan pack includes a pocket schedule, bumper sticker, fan letter, and fan club information (depending on availability).

Directions:	Write your request on paper, and put it in an envelope. You must enclose a **long self-addressed, stamped envelope.**
Write to:	The Chicago Bulls Fan Mail 1901 West Madison Chicago, IL 60612
Ask for:	Chicago Bulls fan pack

Detroit Pistons

Cheer the Pistons on to victory! Send for their fan pack that includes a team schedule and an 8½-by-11-inch team photo (depending on availability).

Directions:	Write your name, address, and request on a postcard.
Write to:	Detroit Pistons Two Championship Drive Auburn Hills, MI 48326 ATTN: Fan Mail
Ask for:	Detroit Pistons fan pack

Atlanta Hawks

The Atlanta Hawks are a team on the rise. Send for this Eastern Conference NBA team's bumper sticker and pocket schedule (depending on availability).

Directions:	Write your request on paper, and put it in an envelope. You must enclose a **long self-addressed, stamped envelope.**
Write to:	Atlanta Hawks PR Department One CNN Center, Suite 405 Atlanta, GA 30303 ATTN: Fan Mail
Ask for:	Atlanta Hawks bumper sticker

Washington Bullets

The Washington Bullets need your support. Their fan pack includes a pocket schedule and bumper sticker (depending on availability).

Directions:	Write your request on paper, and put it in an envelope. You must enclose a **long self-addressed, stamped envelope.**
Write to:	ATTN: Fan Mail Washington Bullets USAir Arena Landover, MD 20785
Ask for:	Washington Bullets fan pack

BASKETBALL

Hall of Fame Pamphlet

Where can you see a pair of bronzed size-22 sneakers? At the Basketball Hall of Fame!
Read all about this "fan-tastic" museum where the history of basketball comes alive.

Directions:	Write your request on paper, and put it in an envelope. You must enclose a **long self-addressed, stamped envelope.**
Write to:	Basketball Hall of Fame 1150 West Columbus Avenue Springfield, MA 01105
Ask for:	HOF pamphlet

Hornets/Heat Stickers

The Miami Heat feature potential all-stars Rony Seiklay and Grant Long. The Charlotte Hornets are home for Alonzo Mourning and Larry "Gran-ma-ma" Johnson. Here's a chance to get team logo stickers for both of these NBA teams. (No substitutions, please.)

Directions:	Write your request on paper, and put it in an envelope. You must enclose a **long self-addressed, stamped envelope** and **$1.00.**
Write to:	Marlene Monroe Department BHT 6210 Ridge Manor Drive Memphis, TN 38115-3411
Ask for:	Charlotte Hornets/Miami Heat stickers

Magic/Suns Stickers

The Orlando Magic have Shaquille O'Neal and Anfernee Hardaway in their lineup, while the Phoenix Suns star Kevin Johnson and Dan Majerle. Now you can get logo stickers for both of these all-star NBA teams. (No substitutions, please.)

Directions:	Write your request on paper, and put it in an envelope. You must enclose a **long self-addressed, stamped envelope** and **$1.00.**
Write to:	Marlene Monroe Department BOP 6210 Ridge Manor Drive Memphis, TN 38115-3411
Ask for:	Orlando Magic/Phoenix Suns stickers

Washington Capitals

"Caps" fans will love this offer from the Washington Capitals. Their fan pack includes team information sheets, schedule, souvenir brochure, and bumper sticker (depending on availability).

Directions:	Write your request on paper, and put it in an envelope. You must enclose a **long self-addressed, stamped envelope.**
Write to:	Washington Capitals ATTN: Fan Mail USAir Arena Landover, MD 20785
Ask for:	Washington Capitals fan pack

Hartford Whalers

Whalers fans will score a hat trick with this fan pack from the NHL's Hartford Whalers. It includes a pocket schedule, team logo sticker, and pamphlet explaining how to join the Junior Whalers fan club (depending on availability).

Directions:	Write your request on paper, and put it in an envelope. You must enclose a **long self-addressed, stamped envelope.**
Write to:	Hartford Whalers Hockey Club 242 Trumbull Street, 8th Floor Hartford, CT 06103 ATTN: Fan Mail
Ask for:	Hartford Whalers fan pack

Florida Panthers

Hockey fans will get a thrill out of this exciting fan pack offered by the NHL's Florida Panthers! It includes a pocket schedule and a team logo sticker (depending on availability).

Directions:	Write your request on paper, and put it in an envelope. You must enclose a **long self-addressed, stamped envelope.**
Write to:	Florida Panthers ATTN: Fan Mail 100 NE Third Avenue, 10th Floor Fort Lauderdale, FL 33301
Ask for:	Florida Panthers fan pack

NHL Stickers

The NHL's expansion has created four hot new hockey teams. Here's your chance to get team stickers of the Tampa Bay Lightning and San Jose Sharks, who began play in 1992, or the Florida Panthers and Anaheim Mighty Ducks, who started up in 1993! (No substitutions, please.)

Directions:	Write your request on paper, and put it in an envelope. You must enclose a **long self-addressed, stamped envelope** and **$1.00.**
Write to:	Marlene Monroe Department NHL 6210 Ridge Manor Drive Memphis, TN 38115-3411
Ask for:	• Lightning/Sharks stickers • Panthers/Mighty Ducks stickers

19

New England Patriots

New England football fans will go for this offer from the New England Patriots! Their fan pack includes a pocket schedule, team logo sticker, and newsletter (depending on availability).

NFL Team Stickers

Here's your chance to get some cool NFL stickers. Choose from the Super Bowl XXVIII teams (Buffalo Bills and Dallas Cowboys) or the NFL expansion teams (Carolina Panthers and Jacksonville Jaguars). (No substitutions, please.)

Directions:	Write your request on paper, and put it in an envelope. You must enclose a **long self-addressed, stamped envelope.**
Write to:	ATTN: Fan Mail New England Patriots Foxboro Stadium 60 Washington Street Foxboro, MA 02035-1388
Ask for:	New England Patriots fan pack

Directions:	Write your request on paper, and put it in an envelope. You must enclose a **long self-addressed, stamped envelope** and **$1.00.**
Write to:	Marlene Monroe Department NFL 6210 Ridge Manor Drive Memphis, TN 38115-3411
Ask for:	• Bills/Cowboys stickers • Panthers/Jaguars stickers

Fishing Decal

If you love fishing, you'll love this decal, too. Stick it on your tackle box or notebook to let others know you enjoy drug-free activities.

GET HOOKED ON FISHING . . .

NOT ON DRUGS!™

FUTURE FISHERMAN FOUNDATION

Directions:	Write your request on paper, and put it in an envelope. You must enclose a **long self-addressed, stamped envelope.**
Write to:	Future Fisherman Foundation 1033 North Fairfax Street, Suite 200 Alexandria, VA 22314
Ask for:	Hooked on Fishing decal

Footbag Membership

Footbag is fun! Learn all about this great sport with an issue of *Footbag World* magazine and a player's manual. You'll even get a lifetime membership card for the World Footbag Association and a cool sticker.

Directions:	Write your request on paper *(include your address, phone number with area code, and date of birth)*, and put it in an envelope. You must enclose **$1.00.**
Write to:	World Footbag Association 1317 Washington Avenue, Suite 7 Golden, CO 80401
Ask for:	Kids' membership

Softball

Softball—the sport of the 1996 Summer Olympic Games—can be your sport, too. Wear this Amateur Softball Association USA Softball pin as a proud member of the ASA·USA softball family. You can also learn more about the ASA youth softball program with this information sheet.

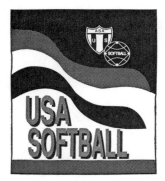

Directions:	Write your request on paper, and put it in an envelope. You must enclose a **long self-addressed, stamped envelope** and **75¢**.
Write to:	Amateur Softball Association USA Softball 2801 NE 50th Street Oklahoma City, OK 73111
Ask for:	USA Softball pin and fact sheet

Soccer

Did you know that soccer is known as football in Europe and that kids all over the world love to play soccer? Send for this illustrated poster with tips to improve your game. You'll also get a colorful patch to wear on your jacket.

Directions:	Write your request on paper, and put it in an envelope. You must enclose **$1.00**.
Write to:	SAY Soccer 4903 Vine Street, Suite #1 Cincinnati, OH 45217
Ask for:	Soccer skills poster and SAY USA patch

Swimming

Dive into this offer! The U.S. Swimming competition isn't just about going for the gold—it's about building a tradition that's as good as gold. Get this decal, and show your support.

Directions:	Write your request on paper, and put it in an envelope. You must enclose a **long self-addressed, stamped envelope.**
Write to:	United States Swimming Marketing Department One Olympic Plaza Colorado Springs, CO 80909
Ask for:	United States Swimming logo decal

Fencing

You might recognize fencing—the art of sword fighting—from movies like *The Three Musketeers, Robin Hood: Prince of Thieves,* and *The Princess Bride.* But did you know fencing is still popular today as an Olympic sport? Learn about fencing's finer points by sending for this brochure.

Directions:	Write your request on paper, and put it in an envelope. You must enclose a **long self-addressed, stamped envelope.**
Write to:	USFA Promotional Department 1750 East Boulder Street Colorado Springs, CO 80909-5774
Ask for:	Spectator brochure

Baseball Cards

For many fans, collecting sports cards is almost as much fun as watching the games. Here's your chance to start your sports-card collection. You'll get five cards with major league baseball stars and stats.

ROGER CLEMENS RED SOX PITCHER

Directions:	Write your request on paper, and put it in an envelope. You must enclose a **long self-addressed, stamped envelope** and **25¢** for **each** set you request.
Write to:	SAV-ON Department MP-3 P.O. Box 1356 Gwinn, MI 49841
Ask for:	Five baseball cards

Photo Sports Button

Who's your favorite professional athlete? Show whom you admire with this photo sports button featuring the NBA, NFL, NHL, or major league baseball star of your choice.

Directions:	Write your request on paper, and put it in an envelope. You must enclose **$1.00** for **each** button you request. *(Please specify the name of the player and the sport that player plays.)*
Write to:	C & B Buttons P.O. Box 650180 Austin, TX 78765
Ask for:	Photo sports button

MEADOWBROOK PRESS
1995 EDITION

U.S. MAIL

STICKERS

Dinosaur Holograms

These dinosaurs look so real, you'll think you're visiting *Jurassic Park*. Send for this cool hologram sticker showing one of these prehistoric giants.

Puffy Dinosaurs

Here are two puffy dinosaur stickers. They'll look great on your notebook or folder and are sure to stick out in a crowd.

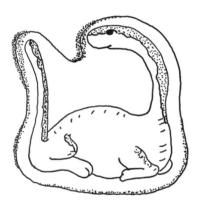

Directions:	Write your request on paper, and put it in an envelope. You must enclose a **long self-addressed, stamped envelope** and **25¢** for **each** sticker you request.
Write to:	SAV-ON Department MP-3 P.O. Box 1356 Gwinn, MI 49841
Ask for:	Dinosaur hologram sticker

Directions:	Write your request on paper, and put it in an envelope. You must enclose a **long self-addressed, stamped envelope** and **25¢** for **each** pair of stickers you request.
Write to:	SAV-ON Department MP-3 P.O. Box 1356 Gwinn, MI 49841
Ask for:	Two puffy dinosaur stickers

Sports Holograms

Here's a set of four fun sports hologram stickers, each featuring a different sport. Give one to your favorite athlete, or stick them on your notebook!

Directions:	Write your request on paper, and put it in an envelope. You must enclose a **long self-addressed, stamped envelope** and **$1.00**.
Write to:	Stickers 'N' Stuff Department SH4 P.O. Box 430 Louisville, CO 80027
Ask for:	Four sports hologram stickers

Sports Stickers

Just do it! These sticker sheets feature baseballs, soccer balls, bowling pins, and more! You'll get two sheets.

Directions:	Write your request on paper, and put it in an envelope. You must enclose a **long self-addressed, stamped envelope** and **$1.00**.
Write to:	Marlene Monroe Department SS 6210 Ridge Manor Drive Memphis, TN 38115-3411
Ask for:	Sports stickers

Looney Toons

The classic Warner Brothers' Looney Toons characters are back! These fun stickers feature Bugs Bunny, Daffy Duck, Elmer Fudd, and more! You'll get two sheets—it's a surprise which ones you'll get!

Garfield Stickers

Garfield is at his food-hungry best in this new set of stickers. You can put them on your notebook or folder, but be sure to hide your lunch! You'll get two sheets.

Directions:	Write your request on paper, and put it in an envelope. You must enclose a **long self-addressed, stamped envelope** and **$1.00.**
Write to:	Marlene Monroe Department LTS 6210 Ridge Manor Drive Memphis, TN 38115-3411
Ask for:	Looney Toons stickers

Directions:	Write your request on paper, and put it in an envelope. You must enclose a **long self-addressed, stamped envelope** and **$1.00.**
Write to:	Marlene Monroe Department GS 6210 Ridge Manor Drive Memphis, TN 38115-3411
Ask for:	Garfield stickers

Disney Classics

Do you enjoy *Bambi, Snow White,* and other classic Disney movies? Then you'll love this set of stickers. You'll get two sheets—it's a surprise which ones you'll get!

Directions:	Write your request on paper, and put it in an envelope. You must enclose a **long self-addressed, stamped envelope** and **$1.00.**
Write to:	Marlene Monroe Department CDS 6210 Ridge Manor Drive Memphis, TN 38115-3411
Ask for:	Classic Disney stickers

Disney Hits

Fans of *The Little Mermaid, Aladdin,* and *Beauty and the Beast* are welcome to sample this set of stickers from recent Disney animated movies. You'll get two sheets—it's a surprise which ones you'll get!

Directions:	Write your request on paper, and put it in an envelope. You must enclose a **long self-addressed, stamped envelope** and **$1.00.**
Write to:	Marlene Monroe Department MDS 6210 Ridge Manor Drive Memphis, TN 38115-3411
Ask for:	Modern Disney stickers

Chrome Stickers

These cute stickers have a shiny appeal. You'll get a dozen metallic-chrome stickers of adorable drawings or animals. They're terrific for brightening up a letter to a friend.

Prism Stickers

A prism captures the colors of the rainbow in shifting light. These prism stickers will make a fascinating addition to your collection. Each sheet contains eight to ten stickers, and you can choose parrots, fish, porpoise, shells, or alligators. You'll get two sheets.

Directions:	Write your request on paper, and put it in an envelope. You must enclose a **long self-addressed, stamped envelope** and **$1.00**.
Write to:	Stickers 'N' Stuff Department KC P.O. Box 430 Louisville, CO 80027
Ask for:	Twelve chrome stickers

Directions:	Write your request on paper, and put it in an envelope. You must enclose a **long self-addressed, stamped envelope** and **$1.00**.
Write to:	DANORS Department S 5721 Funston Street, Bay 14 Hollywood, FL 33023
Ask for:	Two prism sticker sheets

Pearly Stickers

These bright stickers feature all sorts of animals, including cats, bears, puppies, and more. They have a pearl-like look that makes them fun to own. You'll receive twelve sheets of pearlescent stickers plus an exciting sticker catalog.

Directions:	Write your request on paper, and put it in an envelope. You must enclose a **long self-addressed, stamped envelope** and **$1.00.**
Write to:	Stickers 'N' Stuff Department PRL P.O. Box 430 Louisville, CO 80027
Ask for:	Twelve pearlescent sticker sheets

Fuzzy Stickers

This set of cute animal stickers is soft and fuzzy. It feels like you're petting actual animals. You'll receive twelve stickers plus an exciting sticker catalog.

Directions:	Write your request on paper, and put it in an envelope. You must enclose a **long self-addressed, stamped envelope** and **$1.00.**
Write to:	Stickers 'N' Stuff Department FUZ P.O. Box 430 Louisville, CO 80027
Ask for:	Twelve fuzzy stickers

Bright Stickers

Make your sticker collection dazzling with these iridescent stickers. Choose cats, dinosaurs, fish, musical notes, airplanes, or hearts. Pick any two different sheets.

Directions:	Write your request on paper, and put it in an envelope. You must enclose **$1.00**.
Write to:	Lightning Enterprises P.O. Box 16121 West Palm Beach, FL 33416
Ask for:	Iridescent sticker sheets

Glowing Stickers

By day, they look like ordinary stickers; by night, they glow! These glow-in-the-dark stickers will add a friendly shine to your collection. You'll get one sheet with critters and one with moons.

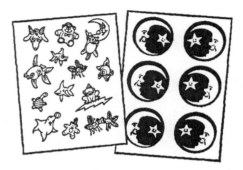

Directions:	Write your request on paper, and put it in an envelope. You must enclose a **long self-addressed, stamped envelope** and **$1.00**.
Write to:	Mr. Rainbows Department P-C4 P.O. Box 908 Rio Grande, NJ 08242
Ask for:	Glow-in-the-dark critters and moons

YUMMY STICKERS

Coca-Cola Stickers

"Trink Coca-Cola" is German for "Drink Coca-Cola." This sticker postcard features the Coke trademark in six different foreign languages, including German, Russian, and Chinese.

Germany

Directions:	Write your name, address, and request on a postcard.
Write to:	The Coca-Cola Company Consumer Information Center Department FS P.O. Drawer 1734 Atlanta, GA 30301
Ask for:	Coca-Cola sticker postcard (limit **one** per request)

Fun Food Stickers

Feeling hungry? These rainbow-colored sticker sheets feature all your favorite fast foods and desserts. You'll get two sheets.

Directions:	Write your request on paper, and put it in an envelope. You must enclose a **long self-addressed, stamped envelope** and **$1.00.**
Write to:	Marlene Monroe Department F 6210 Ridge Manor Drive Memphis, TN 38115-3411
Ask for:	Food stickers

"Thank You" Bears

Here's a colorful way to say "thank you" to a teacher, friend, or parent. These cute stickers feature a bear hugging a big heart that tells everyone exactly how much you appreciate them. You'll get 40 of these fun stickers.

Directions:	Write your request on paper, and put it in an envelope. You must enclose a **long self-addressed, stamped envelope** and **$1.00**.
Write to:	Stickers 'N' Stuff Department TY P.O. Box 430 Louisville, CO 80027
Ask for:	40 "thank you" bear stickers

Hundreds of Stickers

These small, round stickers are colorful, cute, and a great way to highlight a letter to your pen pal or other friends. You'll get one sheet of 100 stickers, and you can choose from either Zoo Crew or Smiles.

Directions:	Write your request on paper, and put it in an envelope. You must enclose **$1.00** for **each** sheet you request.
Write to:	The Very Best Department MP P.O. Box 2838 Long Beach, CA 90801-2838
Ask for:	• 100 Zoo Crew stickers • 100 Smiles stickers

SCHOOL SUPPLIES

Neon Frog Paper

When you're in a funny mood, send a frog-shaped note. This brightly colored stationery is in the shape of a large frog. If you're a nature-lover, you'll love collecting or using this special novelty paper.

Directions:	Write your request on paper, and put it in an envelope. You must enclose a **long self-addressed, stamped envelope** and **25¢** for **each** sheet of stationery you request.
Write to:	The Frog Pond Department K P.O. Box 193 Beech Grove, IN 46107
Ask for:	Frog stationery

Finger Grips

If you do a lot of writing, these colorful finger grips will provide a cushion for your fingers. Just slide them onto your pen or pencil and grip them by the sponge. You'll receive two in different, trendy colors.

Directions:	Write your request on paper, and put it in an envelope. You must enclose **50¢.**
Write to:	ITG Fun Finger Grips P.O. Box 119 Redondo Beach, CA 90277
Ask for:	Two finger grips

Writing Supplies

These writing supplies show others that you say no to drugs and alcohol. You may also ask for an Earth notepad and pencil set to show your commitment to the environment. You'll get two mini notepads and a pencil. *(Please specify which set of writing supplies you want.)*

Directions:	Write your request on paper, and put it in an envelope. You must enclose **$1.00** and **one first-class stamp** for **each** set you request.
Write to:	SAFE Child P.O. Box 40 1594 Brooklyn, NY 11240-1594
Ask for:	• Just Say No notepads and pencil • Our Earth notepads and pencil

Wiggle Ruler and Stickers

This wiggle ruler will keep you at the head of the class. It's twelve-inches long and says, "Just Say No." You'll also get five antidrug stickers.

Directions:	Write your request on paper, and put it in an envelope. You must enclose **$1.00** and **one first-class stamp**.
Write to:	SAFE Child P.O. Box 40 1594 Brooklyn, NY 11240-1594
Ask for:	Just Say No wiggle ruler and stickers

Design Ruler

Now you can create your own masterpieces with this design ruler. It has movable gears and shapes to help you make unique designs. It can even help you with geometry.

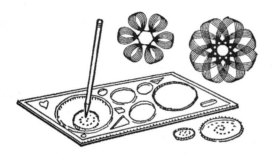

Directions:	Write your request on paper, and put it in an envelope. You must enclose a **long self-addressed, stamped envelope** and **$1.00.**
Write to:	Mr. Rainbows Department M-74 P.O. Box 908 Rio Grande, NJ 08242
Ask for:	Design ruler

Folding Scissors

These scissors are perfect for school. They have colorful handles, come with a carrying case, and cut well. Best of all, they fold up so you can store or carry them safely.

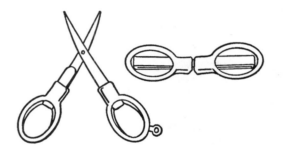

Directions:	Write your request on paper, and put it in an envelope. You must enclose **$1.00.**
Write to:	Eleanor Curran Department S 530 Leonard Street Brooklyn, NY 11222
Ask for:	Folding scissors

Dinosaur Memo Pads

These mini memo pads are great for taking notes in class or writing notes to your friends. Each cover features a different cartoon dinosaur. You'll get three.

Directions:	Write your request on paper, and put it in an envelope. You must enclose **$1.00.**
Write to:	Eleanor Curran Department MM 530 Leonard Street Brooklyn, NY 11222
Ask for:	Dinosaur mini memo pads

Dinosaur Coin Purse

Need a safe place for your change? Then try this vinyl coin purse with a colorful dinosaur on it. With a T-Rex or Brontosaurus guarding your valuables, they're sure to be safe! Comes in a variety of "dino-shapes." You'll get one.

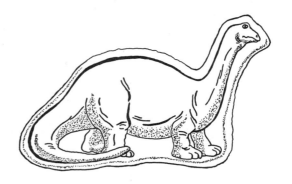

Directions:	Write your request on paper, and put it in an envelope. You must enclose **$1.00.**
Write to:	Eleanor Curran Department DC 530 Leonard Street Brooklyn, NY 11222
Ask for:	Dinosaur coin purse

Sandwich Key Chain

Here's a cute, handy item. It may look like a sandwich, but it's actually a key chain with a hidden mini memo pad that's great for jotting down phone numbers and private thoughts.

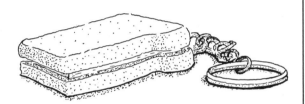

Directions:	Write your request on paper, and put it in an envelope. You must enclose **$1.00.**
Write to:	Lightning Enterprises P.O. Box 16121 West Palm Beach, FL 33416
Ask for:	Secret sandwich notepad–key chain

Yummy Memo Pads

Send a "sweet" note to someone special. These memo pads feature delicious treats on every page. You'll get two.

Directions:	Write your request on paper, and put it in an envelope. You must enclose a **long self-addressed, stamped envelope** and **$1.00.**
Write to:	Mr. Rainbows Department M-24 P.O. Box 908 Rio Grande, NJ 08242
Ask for:	Yummy memo pads

Automatic Pencil

Start writing! Here's a pencil that never needs to be sharpened. You'll get one automatic pencil, a twelve-piece tube of refill lead, and an instruction sheet.

Directions:	Write your request on paper, and put it in an envelope. You must enclose **$1.00.**
Write to:	Pentel's Starter Set Offer 2805 Columbia Street Torrance, CA 90509
Ask for:	Automatic pencil set

Baseball-Bat Pen

Here's a baseball bat you can use in class . . . because it's really a pen! This mini baseball-bat pen is an authentic Louisville Slugger® and is autographed by a famous player.

Directions:	Write your request on paper, and put it in an envelope. You must enclose **$1.00.**
Write to:	H & B Promotions Department 90 SRC P.O. Box 10 Jeffersonville, IN 47130
Ask for:	Louisville Slugger® bat pen

Color Pens

This set of colorful pens is fun and handy. The set contains six colorful pens you can use for outlining, drawing, labeling, and more. Each pen has a small point that's good for detail work, and the set comes in a handy carrying case.

Directions:	Write your request on paper, and put it in an envelope. You must enclose **$1.00.**
Write to:	Pentel's Color Pen Set Offer 2805 Columbia Street Torrance, CA 90509
Ask for:	Pentel color pen set

READING

New Moon Bookmark

New Moon is a magazine for girls and their dreams. It encourages girls to be confident and learn about other cultures. You'll get a nifty bookmark and a pamphlet with more information about this terrific magazine.

Directions:	Write your request on paper, and put it in an envelope. You must enclose a **long self-addressed, stamped envelope.**
Write to:	New Moon P.O. Box 3587 Duluth, MN 55803 ATTN: Bookmark Offer
Ask for:	New Moon bookmark and pamphlet

New Mother Goose

If you've never heard about three *kind* mice or the old lady who lived in a *sandal*, then you'll want this bookmark. These characters can be found in *The New Adventures of Mother Goose*, and this colorful bookmark features five funny new rhymes.

Directions:	Write your request on paper, and put it in an envelope. You must enclose a **long self-addressed, stamped envelope.**
Write to:	Meadowbrook Press Department NMG 18318 Minnetonka Boulevard Deephaven, MN 55391
Ask for:	New Mother Goose bookmark

Personal Bookmark

Reading is more fun with a personalized bookmark keeping your place as you read through your favorite books. This bookmark is laminated and comes with your name on it *(first name only)*.

Directions:	Write your request on paper, and put it in an envelope. You must enclose a **long self-addressed, stamped envelope** and **25¢**.
Write to:	Houser's Unlimited Department FSFK 43826 Birchtree Avenue Lancaster, CA 93534-5011
Ask for:	Personalized bookmark *(please specify the name you want to appear on the bookmark)*

Frog Facts Bookmark

Leap into reading with these colorful frog bookmarks. You'll learn how the tomato frog got its name, how far the gliding frog can glide, how frogs drink water, and other fun frog facts.

Directions:	Write your request on paper, and put it in an envelope. You must enclose a **long self-addressed, stamped envelope** and **50¢** for **each** bookmark you request.
Write to:	The Frog Pond Department K P.O. Box 193 Beech Grove, IN 46107
Ask for:	• Gliding frog bookmark • Tomato frog bookmark

Artprint Bookmark

This vinyl bookmark is strong and attractive. It features a painting or design you might see in a museum. Several designs are available. You'll get one.

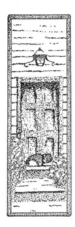

Directions:	Write your request on paper, and put it in an envelope. You must enclose **$1.00.**
Write to:	Joan Nykorchuk 13236 North 7th Street #4 Suite 237 Phoenix, AZ 85022
Ask for:	Artprint bookmark

Book Savers Materials

Treat your books with care, and they'll last a long time. These four bookmarks give you tips on how to care for books. You'll also get a "Read around the House" plastic book bag to protect your books from rain and snow.

Directions:	Write your request on paper, and put it in an envelope. You must enclose a **long self-addressed, stamped envelope** and **$1.00.**
Write to:	Ann Cummings Department 4 106C Witten Circle Havelock, NC 28532
Ask for:	Book savers bookmarks and book bag

"Hug a Book" Button

Do you love to read? Tell the world! Show off your affection for books by wearing this "Hug a Book" button where everyone can see it.

Directions:	Write your request on paper, and put it in an envelope. You must enclose a **long self-addressed, stamped envelope** and **$1.00**.
Write to:	Ann Cummings Department 2 106C Witten Circle Havelock, NC 28532
Ask for:	Hug a Book button

Funny Poetry

A Bad Case of the Giggles is an illustrated book full of hilarious poems chosen by kids your age. Send for this bookmark, featuring a few of the funniest poems from this new book. You'll also get a pamphlet of eight poems from *Kids Pick the Funniest Poems*.

Directions:	Write your request on paper, and put it in an envelope. You must enclose a **long self-addressed, stamped envelope** and **50¢**.
Write to:	Meadowbrook Press Department BCG 18318 Minnetonka Boulevard Deephaven, MN 55391
Ask for:	*A Bad Case of the Giggles* bookmark and Funny Poetry pamphlet

Tough Times Reading List

This pamphlet from the American Library Association lists 50 books that can help you understand and live through troubled times. "Life Can Be Tough" lists books for different age levels that deal with death, divorce, family separation, and other difficulties. Each book offers solutions and raises self-esteem.

Directions:	Write your request on paper, and put it in an envelope. You must enclose a **long self-addressed, stamped envelope.**
Write to:	American Library Association Graphics Department LCBT 50 East Huron Street Chicago, IL 60611
Ask for:	Life Can Be Tough pamphlet

Multicultural Reading List

The United States is a unique country, made up of people from across the world, who bring their own traditions and beliefs to our country, enriching us all. This reading list starts you off as you learn about the different cultures of America.

Directions:	Write your request on paper, and put it in an envelope. You must enclose a **long self-addressed, stamped envelope.**
Write to:	American Library Association Graphics Department MFMS 50 East Huron Street Chicago, IL 60611
Ask for:	Many Faces, Many Stories pamphlet

Reading Pamphlet

Each year the Coretta Scott King award goes to African-American authors and illustrators whose children's books promote a better understanding of black culture. Send for this pamphlet that lists the award winners and their titles.

CORETTA SCOTT KING AWARD
AND HONOR BOOKS

Directions:	Write your request on paper, and put it in an envelope. You must enclose a **long self-addressed, stamped envelope.**
Write to:	American Library Association Graphics Department CSK 50 East Huron Street Chicago, IL 60611
Ask for:	Coretta Scott King pamphlet

Reading List

Children of color living in America today experience the ups and downs, joys and tears that are part of everyone's childhood. Here's a list of books about "Today's Children of Color" as they go through first love, grow up with brothers and sisters, live with (or without) parents, and have fun.

Directions:	Write your request on paper, and put it in an envelope. You must enclose a **long self-addressed, stamped envelope.**
Write to:	American Library Association Graphics Department TCOC 50 East Huron Street Chicago, IL 60611
Ask for:	Today's Children of Color reading list

Jump-Rope Rhymes

Start skipping! Here's a mini book that fits in your pocket with the words to 29 jump-rope rhymes. You'll find "Fudge, Fudge," "Miss Lucey Had a Baby," and more!

Directions:	Write your request on paper, and put it in an envelope. You must enclose a **long self-addressed, stamped envelope** and **$1.00.**
Write to:	Practical Parenting Department FS-JR Deephaven, MN 55391-3275
Ask for:	Jump-Rope Rhymes booklet

Fairy Tale Cards

Do you love tales like "Cinderella" and "Jack and the Beanstalk"? These colorful six-panel cards tell and illustrate your favorite fairy tales. They also fold up into neat packages you can send to friends without using envelopes.

Directions:	Write your request on paper, and put it in an envelope. You must enclose a **long self-addressed, stamped envelope** and **$1.00** for **each** card you request.
Write to:	More Than A Card 4334 Earhart Boulevard New Orleans, LA 70125
Ask for:	• Snow White book-card • Hansel and Gretel book-card • Jack and the Beanstalk book-card • Cinderella book-card • Rumpelstiltskin book-card • Little Red Riding Hood book-card

Surprises Magazine

If you enjoy puzzles, mazes, or crosswords, you'll love *Surprises*. This exciting magazine overflows with educational games and activities, jokes and riddles, arts and craft ideas, and more.

Directions:	Write your request on paper, and place it in an envelope. You must enclose **$1.00.**
Write to:	*Surprises* Samples Department 1200 North Seventh Street Minneapolis, MN 55411
Ask for:	Sample copy of *Surprises*

Dolphin Log Magazine

The Cousteau Society cares about all forms of marine life, from whales to starfish. Their magazine, *Dolphin Log,* will help you learn to care, too. Find out about marine animals like the manatee and how people are working to protect them.

Directions:	Write your request on paper, and put it in an envelope. You must enclose **$1.00.**
Write to:	The Cousteau Society 870 Greenbriar Circle, Suite 402 Chesapeake, VA 23320 ATTN: Victoria Robinson
Ask for:	*Dolphin Log* sample

For Young Readers

Explore these exciting magazines by yourself or with a grown-up. *Turtle* (ages 2 to 5) has hidden pictures, dot-to-dots, coloring pages, and more. *Humpty Dumpty's* (ages 4 to 6) features fun stories, poems, and puzzles. *Children's Playmate* (ages 6 to 8) offers games, recipes, cartoons, and activities.

Directions:	Write your request on paper, and put it in an envelope. You must enclose **$1.00** for **each** magazine you request.
Write to:	Children's Better Health Institute Department FSFK5 1100 Waterway Boulevard Indianapolis, IN 46202 ATTN: Chelle
Ask for:	• *Turtle* magazine • *Humpty Dumpty's* magazine • *Children's Playmate* magazine

For Older Readers

These three magazines invite you to laugh, learn, and create. *Jack and Jill* (ages 7 to 10) has jokes, activities, and works by kids. *Child Life* (ages 9 to 11) features Odd Jobs career profiles and Diane's Dinosaur comics. *Children's Digest* (preteen) offers contemporary fiction, articles on important issues, and book reviews.

Directions:	Write your request on paper, and put it in an envelope. You must enclose **$1.00** for **each** magazine you request.
Write to:	Children's Better Health Institute Department FSFK5 1100 Waterway Boulevard Indianapolis, IN 46202 ATTN: Chelle
Ask for:	• *Jack and Jill* magazine • *Child Life* magazine • *Children's Digest* magazine

MATH AND SCIENCE

Financial Comic Books

Don't wait until college to start learning about how our economy works. Here are five comic books to help you understand basic economics, like banking, inflation, and foreign trade. Specify which comic books you want.

Directions:	Write your name, address, and request on a postcard.
Write to:	Federal Reserve Bank of New York Public Information Department 33 Liberty Street, 13th Floor New York, NY 10045
Ask for:	• *Story of Banks* comic book • *Too Much, Too Little* comic book • *The Story of Inflation* comic book • *Story of Foreign Trade* comic book • *Once Upon a Dime* comic book

Money Trivia Quiz

What is money? You might be surprised to find out that a dollar represents one ounce of silver. Send for this money trivia quiz to learn more about money, its origins, and why it's valuable.

Directions:	Write your request on paper, and put it in an envelope. You must enclose a **long self-addressed, stamped envelope** and **50¢.**
Write to:	Money Trivia Bluestocking Press Department FS 95 P.O. Box 1014 Placerville, CA 95667
Ask for:	Money Trivia Quiz pamphlet

Space Ruler

Explore another world. This ruler has colorful holograms of astronauts and spacecrafts that move as you convert from inches to centimeters.

Directions:	Write your request on paper, and put it in an envelope. You must enclose **$1.00.**
Write to:	IPM Department FS-1 P.O. Box 1181 Hammond, IN 46325
Ask for:	Space ruler

Solar System Facts

You can have solar system facts right at your fingertips with this handy chart. Find the average length of a year on Pluto, the temperature on Venus, or the atmosphere on Mars.

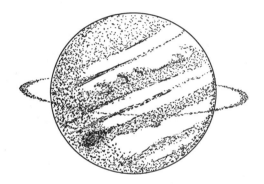

Directions:	Write your request on paper, and put it in an envelope. You must enclose a **long self-addressed, stamped envelope** and **25¢.**
Write to:	Solar System Education Department Hansen Planetarium 15 South State Street Salt Lake City, UT 84111-1590
Ask for:	Solar system fact sheet

Space Hologram Cards

Far out! Here's a set of hologram cards featuring scenes from space. The backs of the cards have interesting facts about space missions, astronauts, and the space program.

Directions:	Write your request on paper, and put it in an envelope. You must enclose **$1.00.**
Write to:	Joan Nykorchuk 13236 North 7th Street #4 Suite 237 Phoenix, AZ 85022
Ask for:	Four space hologram cards

Fuzzy Earth Stickers

Show everyone you care about the environment. These fuzzy stickers feature teddy bears hugging the earth.

Directions:	Write your request on paper, and put it in an envelope. You must enclose a **long self-addressed, stamped envelope** and **$1.00**.
Write to:	Mr. Rainbows Department P-24 P.O. Box 908 Rio Grande, NJ 08242
Ask for:	Fuzzy earth stickers

Ocean Saver Pamphlet

Learn how you can make a difference to the environment. This pamphlet gives tips on what you can do every day to save water, keep oceans cleaner, and recycle.

Directions:	Write your request on paper, and put it in an envelope. You must enclose a **long self-addressed, stamped envelope**.
Write to:	Schneider Educational Products P.O. Box 472260 San Francisco, CA 94147
Ask for:	I'm an Ocean Saver pamphlet

Science Experiments

Thanks to the *Newton's Apple* TV show and 3M, you can have six fascinating science experiments! With this "Science Try-Its™" sheet, you'll be able to perform fun, easy science experiments at home.

Directions:	Write your request on paper, and put it in an envelope. You must enclose a **long self-addressed, stamped envelope.**
Write to:	Newton's Apple Science Try-Its c/o Twin Cities Public Television 172 East Fourth Street Saint Paul, MN 55101
Ask for:	Science Try-Its™

Science Newsletter

Join the Science for Every Kid Club and receive this informative newsletter. It features science and earthcare information, science activities, word puzzles, and more!

Directions:	Write your request on paper, and put it in an envelope. You must enclose a **long self-addressed, stamped envelope.**
Write to:	John Wiley & Sons 605 Third Avenue New York, NY 10158 ATTN: Fred Nachbaur
Ask for:	Science for Every Kid Newsletter

Solar Hot-Dog Cooker

Learn how to cook a hot dog without using a stove or microwave! These instructions tell you how to build a solar-powered hot-dog cooker from cardboard and aluminum foil—fascinating and fun for anyone who's into solar energy.

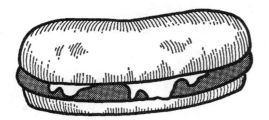

Directions:	Write your request on paper, and put it in an envelope. You must enclose a **long self-addressed, stamped envelope** and **50¢**.
Write to:	Energy and Marine Center Department FS-95 P.O. Box 190 Port Richey, FL 34673
Ask for:	Solar hot-dog cooker instructions

Model Skeleton

This skeleton's a great introduction to basic anatomy. You'll get an eight-inch rubber skeleton and a cute poem. It's fun as a learning tool or for hanging in your window during Halloween.

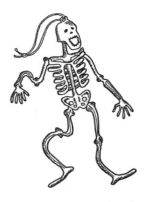

Directions:	Write your request on a piece of paper, and put it in an envelope. You must enclose a **long self-addressed, stamped envelope** with **two first-class stamps** on it and **$1.00**.
Write to:	Reading Realm Department B P.O. Box 274 Barker, TX 77413-0274
Ask for:	My Bones skeleton and poem

Coal Booklets

Where does coal come from? How is it used? How does it affect the environment? Find the answers to these and other questions in these three booklets from the American Coal Foundation. Please specify the booklets you want.

Directions:	Write your name, address, and request on a postcard.
Write to:	American Coal Foundation 1130 17th Street NW, Suite 220 Washington, DC 20036
Ask for:	• Let's Learn about Coal booklet • Power from Coal booklet • Electricity from Coal booklet

Story of Cotton Booklet

Did you know the ancient Egyptians made and wore cotton clothing? Cotton has been around for centuries and is currently the leading cash crop in the U.S. This booklet will show you where cotton grows and how it's harvested, ginned, and marketed.

Directions:	Write your name, address, and request on a postcard.
Write to:	National Cotton Council Communications Services Department Box 12285 Memphis, TN 38182
Ask for:	The Story of Cotton booklet

MEADOWBROOK PRESS
1995 EDITION

U.S.
MAIL

AMERICAN HISTORY AND GEOGRAPHY

George Washington

Did you know that George Washington never chopped down a cherry tree or wore a wig? Learn fascinating facts about his life and presidency from this collection of brochures, booklets, and postcards. You'll also get excerpts from his boyhood journal, a brief biography, and a "scratch and learn" quiz card.

Directions:	Write your request on paper, and put it in an envelope. You must enclose **$1.00**.
Write to:	Mount Vernon Ladies' Association Education Department Mount Vernon, VA 22121
Ask for:	George Washington materials for kids

Laura Ingalls Wilder

Did you enjoy the TV show *Little House on the Prairie?* Then you'll be interested in this timeline detailing the life and times of the real Laura Ingalls Wilder and her daughter, Rose Wilder Lane.

Directions:	Write your request on paper, and put it in an envelope. You must enclose a **long self-addressed, stamped envelope** and **$1.00**.
Write to:	Bluestocking Press Department FSK P.O. Box 1014 Placerville, CA 95667
Ask for:	Laura Ingalls Wilder timeline

Native Americans

Learn all about the Cherokee—their history, culture, leaders, and more. These materials from the Cherokee National Historical Society will help you better understand these fascinating people.

Directions:	Write your name, address, and request on a postcard.
Write to:	Cherokee National Historical Society Carol Dunn, Education Department P.O. Box 515 Tahlequah, OK 74465
Ask for:	Cherokee information

Howdy Pardner Materials

Everyone seems to know something about cowboys in the Old West. But did you know that cowboys still exist? Send for this offer from the National Cowboy Hall of Fame. You'll get a Howdy Pardner Club pencil and an informative brochure.

Directions:	Write your request on paper, and put it in an envelope. You must enclose a **long self-addressed, stamped envelope** and **25¢.** *(Please indicate the state in which you live.)*
Write to:	National Cowboy Hall of Fame Public Relations Department 1700 NE 63rd Street Oklahoma City, OK 73111
Ask for:	Howdy Pardner Club pencil and brochure

Civil War Site

The most famous battle of the American Civil War took place in Gettysburg, Pennsylvania. Today the town honors that battle with more than 1,000 monuments and other attractions. This 64-page guide tells you all about Gettysburg.

Directions:	Write your name, address, and request on a postcard.
Write to:	Gettysburg Travel Council Department 501 35 Carlisle Street Gettysburg, PA 17325
Ask for:	Gettysburg tourism booklet

History of Paper

Trace the history of paper in the United States with this large poster. You can also get materials with information about paper's environmental impact, paper recycling, and instructions for how to make your own paper. Specify which items you want.

Directions:	Write your name, address, and request on a postcard.
Write to:	American Forest & Paper Association 1111 19th Street NW Washington, DC 20036
Ask for:	• How Paper Came to America poster • Paper and Paper Manufacture booklet • How You Can Make Paper foldout

Flag House Materials

The Battle of Baltimore, during the War of 1812, sparked Francis Scott Key's writing of *The Star-Spangled Banner*, our national anthem. These materials about the American flag and Fort McHenry will teach you more. You'll also get a copy of the original *Star-Spangled Banner* song.

Directions:	Write your request on paper, and put it in an envelope. You must enclose **$1.00**.
Write to:	The Star-Spangled Banner Flag House Corner of Albemarle Street 844 East Pratt Street Baltimore, MD 21202
Ask for:	Flag House materials for kids

American-Flag Patch

Show your patriotism! You can sew this American-flag patch to your jacket, baseball cap, or backpack.

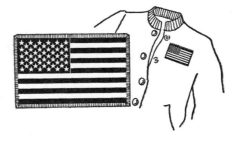

Directions:	Write your request on paper, and put it in an envelope. You must enclose a **long self-addressed, stamped envelope** and **50¢**.
Write to:	Pineapple Appeal Department FS Box 197 Owatonna, MN 55060
Ask for:	American-flag patch

Your Birthday's History

Find out your birthday's place in history. This fact sheet tells you what special events happened the day and year you were born. You'll learn which famous people share your birthday, what the top songs and movies were, and more!

Directions:	Write your request on paper, and put it in an envelope. You must enclose a **long self-addressed, stamped envelope** and **$1.00.** *(Please include your birthday, age, and state you were born in.)*
Write to:	Special Products Department FS-1 34 Romeyn Avenue Amsterdam, NY 12010
Ask for:	Happy Birthday sheet

Be a Pen Pal

Learn about other parts of America without leaving your house. A pen pal is a special friend you write letters to—you can share information about your state, neighborhood, school, and family with another kid your age who shares similar interests. The Dolphin Pen Pal Center will send you the address of your new pen pal so you can start writing.

Directions:	Write your request on paper *(and include your age, grade, and favorite activities)*, and put it in an envelope. You must enclose a **long self-addressed, stamped envelope** and **$1.00.**
Write to:	Dolphin Pen Pal Center Department FS5 32-B Shelter Cove Lane Hilton Head Island, SC 29928
Ask for:	U.S. pen pal

America's Sites

The United States has a wealth of history and natural beauty. Now you can explore America's sites, parks, and monuments with these informative publications.

Directions:	Write your name, address, and request on a postcard.
Write to:	The tourism offices listed here
Ask for:	Tourism information

Booker T. Washington
Booker T. Washington National Monument
Route 3, Box 310
Hardy, VA 24101

Carlsbad Caverns
Carlsbad Caverns National Park
3225 National Parks Highway
Carlsbad, NM 88220

Custer's Last Stand
Little Big Horn National Monument
P.O. Box 39
Crow Agency, MT 59022

Death Valley
Death Valley National Monument
Death Valley, CA 92328

Dinosaurs
Dinosaur National Monument
P.O. Box 210
Dinosaur, CO 81610

Edison National Historic Site
Main Street and Lakeside Avenue
West Orange, NJ 07052

Frederick Douglass National Historic Site
1411 W Street SE
Washington, DC 20020

Fort Sumter
Fort Sumter National Monument
1214 Middle Street
Sullivan's Island, SC 29482

Grand Teton
Grand Teton National Park
P.O. Drawer 170
Moose, WY 83012

Ice Age
Ice Age Trail Project
700 Ray-O-Vac Drive, Suite 100
Madison, WI 53711

Lewis and Clark
Lewis and Clark National Historic Trail
700 Ray-O-Vac Drive, Suite 100
Madison, WI 53711

Lincoln Memorial
c/o National Park Service
NCP-Central
900 Ohio Drive SW
Washington, DC 20242

Martin Luther King Jr. National Historic Site
526 Auburn Avenue NE
Atlanta, GA 30312

SEE THE U.S.A.

Montezuma Castle
Montezuma Castle National Monument
P.O. Box 219
Camp Verde, AZ 86322

Monticello
Virginia State Chamber of Commerce
9 South Fifth Street
Richmond, VA 23219

Mount Rushmore
Mount Rushmore National Monument
P.O. Box 268
Keystone, SD 57751-0268

Mount Vernon
Virginia State Chamber of Commerce
9 South Fifth Street
Richmond, VA 23219

Nez Perce
Nez Perce National Historic Park
P.O. Box 93
Spalding, ID 83551

North Country
North Country
700 Ray-O-Vac Drive, Suite 100
Madison, WI 53711

San Antonio
San Antonio Missions National Historic Park
2202 Roosevelt Avenue
San Antonio, TX 78210-4919

Sunset Crater/Wupatki National Monuments
Route 3, Box 149
Flagstaff, AZ 86004

Thomas Jefferson Memorial
c/o National Park Service
NCP-Central
900 Ohio Drive SW
Washington, DC 20242

Valley Forge
Valley Forge Convention and Visitors Bureau
P.O. Box 331
Norristown, PA 19404

Vietnam Veterans Memorial
c/o National Park Service
NCP-Central
900 Ohio Drive SW
Washington, DC 20242

Washington Monument
c/o National Park Service
NCP-Central
900 Ohio Drive SW
Washington, DC 20242

White House
National Capitol Region
National Park Service
President's Park
1100 Ohio Drive SW
Washington, DC 20242

Williamsburg
Director of Media Relations
Colonial Williamsburg Foundation
P.O. Box 1776
Williamsburg, VA 23187

Wisconsin Dells Visitor and Convention Bureau
701 Superior Street
Wisconsin Dells, WI 53965

Discover America

Whether you're planning a family trip or are just curious about your country, you'll want to send for these state and city tourism packets. Every state listed here will send something special.

Directions:	Write your name, address, and request on a postcard.
Write to:	The state offices listed here
Ask for:	Tourism information

Alabama
Alabama Bureau of Tourism & Travel
401 Adams Avenue
Montgomery, AL 36104

Greater Birmingham Convention & Visitors Center
2200 Ninth Avenue North
Birmingham, AL 35203

Alaska
Alaska Division of Tourism
P.O. Box 110801
Juneau, AK 99811-0801

Anchorage Convention & Visitors Bureau
1600 A Street, Suite 200
Anchorage, AK 99501

Arizona
Arizona Office of Tourism
1100 West Washington
Phoenix, AZ 85007

Phoenix and Valley of the Sun
  Convention & Visitors Bureau
1 Arizona Plaza
400 East Van Buren, Suite 600
Phoenix, AZ 85004-2290

Arkansas
Tourism Division
Arkansas Department of Parks & Tourism
One Capitol Mall
Little Rock, AR 72201

Greater Little Rock Chamber of Commerce
One Spring Building
Little Rock, AR 72201

California
California Office of Tourism
801 K Street, Suite 1600
Sacramento, CA 95814

Los Angeles Convention & Visitors Bureau
633 West Fifth Street, Suite 6000
Los Angeles, CA 90071

San Diego Convention & Visitors Bureau
1200 Third Avenue, Suite 824
San Diego, CA 92101

Colorado
Colorado Tourism Board
1625 Broadway, Suite 1700
Denver, CO 80202

Connecticut
Department of Economic Development
Tourism Division
865 Brook Street
Rocky Hill, CT 06067-3405

Delaware
Delaware Development Office
99 Kings Highway
P.O. Box 1401
Dover, DE 19903

District of Columbia
Washington Convention & Visitors Association
1212 New York Avenue NW, 6th Floor
Washington, DC 20005

Florida
Florida Division of Tourism Services
Bureau of Visitor Services
107 West Gaines Street, Room 501D
Tallahassee, FL 32399-2000

Jacksonville Convention & Visitors Bureau
3 Independent Drive
Jacksonville, FL 32202

Greater Miami Convention & Visitors Bureau
701 Brickell Avenue, Suite 2700
Miami, FL 33131

Georgia
Atlanta Convention & Visitors Bureau
233 Peachtree Street, Suite 2000
Atlanta, GA 30303

Georgia Department of Industry & Trade
Tourist Division
P.O. Box 1776
Atlanta, GA 30301

Hawaii
Hawaii Visitors Bureau
2270 Kalakaua Avenue
Honolulu, HI 96815

Idaho
Idaho Department of Commerce
State House Mail
700 West State Street
Boise, ID 83720-2700

Illinois
Department of Commerce & Community Affairs
Information and Distribution Center
620 East Adams Street, Floor M1
Springfield, IL 62701

Illinois Tourist Information Center
100 West Randolph Street, Suite 3-400
Chicago, IL 60601

Indiana
Tourism Development
Department of Commerce
1 North Capitol, Suite 700
Indianapolis, IN 46204

Iowa
Division of Tourism
200 East Grand
Des Moines, IA 50309

Kansas
Kansas Travel & Tourism Information
Department of Commerce
700 SW Harrison, Suite 1300
Topeka, KS 66603

Kentucky
Tourism Cabinet
Capitol Plaza Tower
500 Mero Street, Suite 22
Frankfort, KY 40601

Convention & Visitors Bureau
400 South First Street
Louisville, KY 40202

Louisiana
Louisiana Office of Tourism
Inquiries Station
P.O. Box 94291
Baton Rouge, LA 70804-9291

Greater New Orleans Tourism & Convention
  Commission
1520 Sugar Bowl Drive
New Orleans, LA 70112

Maine
Department of Economic & Community Development
Office of Tourism
193 State Street
Augusta, ME 04333

Maryland
Office of Tourism
Visitors Center
23 West Chesapeake
Towson, MD 21204

Baltimore Area and Information Center
300 West Pratt Street
Baltimore, MD 21201

Massachusetts
Massachusetts Travel & Tourism
100 Cambridge Street, 13th Floor
Boston, MA 02202

Greater Boston Convention & Visitors Bureau
Prudential Tower
P.O. Box 490, Suite 400
Boston, MA 02199

Michigan
Michigan Travel Bureau
P.O. Box 30226
Lansing, MI 48909

Metropolitan Detroit Convention & Visitors Bureau
100 Renaissance Center, Suite 1950
Detroit, MI 48243-1056

Flint Convention & Visitors Bureau
Northbank Center, Suite 101-A
400 North Saginaw
Flint, MI 48502

Minnesota
Minnesota Office of Tourism
100 Metro Square Building
121 Seventh Place East
Saint Paul, MN 55101

Greater Minneapolis Convention &
  Visitors Association
1219 Marquette Avenue South, Suite 300
Minneapolis, MN 55403

Saint Paul Convention & Visitors Bureau
101 Norwest Center
55 East Fifth Street
Saint Paul, MN 55101-1713

Mississippi
Mississippi Division of Tourism
P.O. Box 849
Jackson, MS 39205-0849

Natchez Convention & Visitors Commission
P.O. Box 1485
Natchez, MS 39121

Missouri
Convention & Visitors Bureau of Greater Kansas City
City Square Center
1100 Main Street, Suite 2550
Kansas City, MO 64105

Convention & Visitors Bureau of Greater Saint Louis
10 South Broadway, Suite 1000
Saint Louis, MO 63102

Montana
Montana Department of Commerce
Travel Promotion
1424 Ninth Avenue
Helena, MT 59620

Nebraska
Nebraska Department of Economic Development
Travel & Tourism Division
301 Centennial Mall South
P.O. Box 94666
Lincoln, NE 68509

Nevada
Nevada Commission of Tourism
5151 South Carson Street
Carson City, NV 89710

Las Vegas Convention & Visitors Authority
3150 South Paradise Road
Las Vegas, NV 89109

New Hampshire
Department of Resources & Economic Development
Division of Parks & Recreation
172 Pembroke Road
Concord, NH 03301

New Jersey
New Jersey Division of Tourism
P.O. Box CN 826
Trenton, NJ 08625

Atlantic City Convention & Visitors Bureau
2301 Boardwalk
Atlantic City, NJ 08401

New Mexico
New Mexico Department of Tourism
Lamy Building
491 Old Sante Fe Trail
Santa Fe, NM 87503

New York
New York Convention & Visitors Bureau
Two Columbus Circle
New York, NY 10019

North Carolina
North Carolina Department of Commerce
Travel & Tourism Division
430 North Salisbury Street
Raleigh, NC 27603

Charlotte Convention & Visitors Bureau
122 East Stonewall Street
Charlotte, NC 28202

North Dakota
North Dakota Travel Department
Liberty Memorial Building
604 East Boulevard
Bismarck, ND 58505

Ohio
Ohio Office of Travel & Tourism
77 South High Street, 29th Floor
Columbus, OH 43266

Greater Cincinnati Convention & Visitors Bureau
300 West Sixth Street
Cincinnati, OH 45202

Oklahoma
Oklahoma Tourism & Recreation Department
2401 North Lincoln Boulevard, Suite 500
Oklahoma City, OK 73105-4492

Oregon
Oregon Tourism Division
775 Summer Street NE
Salem, OR 97310

Portland/Oregon Visitors Association
26 SW Salmon Street
Portland, OR 97204-3299

Pennsylvania
Pennsylvania Department of Commerce
Bureau of Travel Development
453 Forum Building
Harrisburg, PA 17120

Philadelphia Convention & Visitors Bureau
1515 Market Street, Suite 2020
Philadelphia, PA 19102

Greater Pittsburgh Convention & Visitors Bureau
4 Gateway Center, Suite 514
Pittsburgh, PA 15222

Rhode Island
Rhode Island Department of Economic Development
Tourist Promotion Division
Seven Jackson Walkway
Providence, RI 02903

South Carolina
South Carolina Department of Parks,
   Recreation, & Tourism
Division of Tourism
1205 Pendleton Street
Columbia, SC 29201

South Dakota
South Dakota Department of Tourism
711 East Wells Avenue
Pierre, SD 57501-3369

Tennessee
Tennessee Tourist Development
P.O. Box 23170
Nashville, TN 37202

Knoxville Convention & Visitors Bureau
P.O. Box 15012
Knoxville, TN 37901

Memphis Convention & Visitors Bureau
45 Union Avenue
Memphis, TN 38103

Texas
Texas Department of Commerce
Tourism Division
P.O. Box 12728
Austin, TX 78711

Dallas Convention & Visitors Bureau
1201 Elm Street, Suite 2000
Dallas, TX 75270

Fort Worth Convention & Visitors Bureau
415 Throckmorton Street
Fort Worth, TX 76102

Utah
Utah Travel Council
Council Hall, Capitol Hill
Salt Lake City, UT 84114

Salt Lake Convention & Visitors Bureau
180 South West Temple
Salt Lake City, UT 84101-1493

Vermont
Vermont Travel Division
134 State Street
Montpelier, VT 05602

Virginia
Virginia Division of Tourism
1021 East Cary
Richmond, VA 23219

Norfolk Convention & Visitors Bureau
236 East Plume Street
Norfolk, VA 23510

Washington
Department of Trade & Economic Development
Tourism Department Division
P.O. 42500
Olympia, WA 98504-2500

Seattle–King County Convention & Visitors Bureau
520 Pike Street, Suite 1300
Seattle, WA 98101

West Virginia
West Virginia Division of Tourism & Parks
1900 Kanawha Boulevard
Building 6, Room B564
Charleston, WV 25305-0317

Wisconsin
Wisconsin Tourism
P.O. Box 7970
Madison, WI 53707

Greater Milwaukee Convention & Visitors Bureau
510 West Kilbourn
Milwaukee, WI 53203

Wyoming
Wyoming Travel Commission
I-25 at College Drive
Cheyenne, WY 82002

Casper Area Chamber of Commerce
P.O. Box 399
500 North Center
Casper, WY 82601

ANIMALS AND THE ENVIRONMENT

Sea Otters

The southern sea otter, hunted almost to extinction for its fur, now faces threats from oil spills and other sources. To learn more about sea otters and ways you can help save them, send for this education packet and official Friends of the Sea Otter sticker.

Animal Welfare

The efforts of one man, Brian Davies, helped stop the commercial hunt of baby harp and hood seals. It took over twenty years, but they are now out of danger. His International Fund for Animal Welfare (IFAW) is still at work, saving animals from cruelty worldwide. Send for their materials to find out more.

Directions:	Write your request on paper, and put it in an envelope. You must enclose **one first-class stamp.**
Write to:	Friends of the Sea Otter 2150 Garden Road Suite B4 Monterey, CA 93940
Ask for:	Education packet and sticker

Directions:	Write your name, address, and request on a postcard.
Write to:	IFAW P.O. Box 193, Building 2 Yarmouth Port, MA 02675
Ask for:	Fact sheets and animal stickers

Beavers

Beavers help conserve water and prevent drought and flood. But many beavers are killed for their fur or when their work interferes with that of humans. Now you can help! Read about the Beaver Defenders, a friendly beaver named Chopper, and how to get involved.

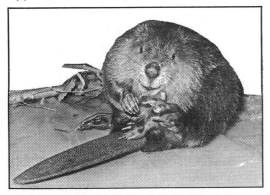

Directions:	Write your request on paper, and put it in an envelope. You must enclose a **long self-addressed, stamped envelope.**
Write to:	The Beaver Defenders P.O. Box 765 Newfield, NJ 08344
Ask for:	Beaver information

The Wildlife of Africa

Some African animals—like rhinos, elephants, and gorillas—are endangered because of hunting. Learn about these species with information packets from the African Wildlife Foundation. You may also send for a bumper sticker that reads, "Only Elephants Should Wear Ivory." Specify which items you want.

ONLY ELEPHANTS SHOULD WEAR IVORY
AFRICAN WILDLIFE FOUNDATION
WASHINGTON, D.C. CALL 1-800-344-TUSK OR 202-265-8393   NAIROBI, KENYA CALL 23235

Directions:	Write your name, address, and request on a postcard.
Write to:	African Wildlife Foundation 1717 Massachusetts Avenue NW Suite 602 Washington, DC 20036
Ask for:	• Rhino info • Elephant info • Gorilla info • Bumper sticker

Be Kind to Animals

A little kindness can go a long way! Discover the many steps you can take to save animals by sending for these free materials.

Directions:	Write your request on paper, and put it in an envelope. You must enclose a **long self-addressed, stamped envelope.**
Write to:	ISAR Department A 421 South State Street Clarks Summit, PA 18411
Ask for:	Free informational materials

Preserve Wetlands

Many of nature's animals depend on wetland preserves and wildlife refuges to protect them against overhunting. Learn how to help preserve these lands by collecting duck stamps. This pamphlet from the Consumer Information Center gives you all the details.

Directions:	Write your name, address, and request on a postcard.
Write to:	Consumer Information Center Department 576A Pueblo, CO 81009
Ask for:	The Duck Stamp Story pamphlet

Pet Care

Saving animals can start in your own home. Your pet is a member of your family, so it's important to give it proper care. This pamphlet tells what a veterinary exam is all about. You'll also get a nifty "Caring Kids Care for Pets" sticker to show you're a kid who cares about animals.

Directions:	Write your request on paper, and put it in an envelope. You must enclose a **long self-addressed, stamped envelope.**
Write to:	American Animal Hospital Assn. P.O. Box 150899 Denver, CO 80215-0899 ATTN: MSC
Ask for:	Health Exams pamphlet and Caring Kids sticker

Conservation Poster

The Nature Conservancy works to protect the world's animal and plant life by purchasing the deserts, mountains, and wetlands where endangered species live. One way you can help is by learning about conservation and ecosystems from this coloring poster.

The Nature Conservancy

Directions:	Write your name, address, and request on a postcard.
Write to:	The Nature Conservancy Member Relations 1815 North Lynn Street Arlington, VA 22209
Ask for:	Coloring poster

Bird Stickers

If you're a bird lover, here's an offer you'll really appreciate. These colorful 1½-inch-round stickers feature a bald eagle, owl, pelican, robin, cardinal, and bluejay. You'll get six stickers.

Directions:	Write your request on paper, and put it in an envelope. You must enclose a **long self-addressed, stamped envelope** and **$1.00**.
Write to:	Mr. Rainbows Department DR-35 P.O. Box 908 Rio Grande, NJ 08242
Ask for:	Environmental bird stickers

Wilderness Society

The Wilderness Society knows that protecting America's forests, deserts, and wetlands also helps protect the animals who live there. Learn more about it with this fact sheet. You'll also get some wilderness stamps.

Directions:	Write your request on paper, and put it in an envelope. You must enclose a **long, self-addressed, stamped envelope.**
Write to:	The Wilderness Society Membership Services, FSFK 900 17th Street NW Washington, DC 20006-2596
Ask for:	Fact sheet and wilderness stamps *(Teachers—please order only one packet per classroom.)*

Delta Society

The Delta Society believes that animals improve the lives and well-being of people. They also believe that people can improve the lives and well-being of animals. To learn how, send for their list of books on human-to-animal relationships.

Directions:	Write your request on paper, and put it in an envelope. You must enclose a **long self-addressed, stamped envelope.**
Write to:	DELTA SOCIETY® P.O. Box 1080 Renton, WA 98057-1080
Ask for:	Free materials for kids

Dissection

You might be asked to "dissect" in a science class at school—this means cutting up a dead animal in order to study it. If you feel sad or uncomfortable about this, it's okay. The National Anti-Vivisection Society is behind you and has a handbook that helps explain the issue and your choices.

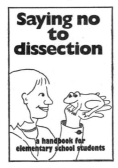

Directions:	Write your name, address, and request on a postcard or call 1-800-922-FROG. *(Include your grade.)*
Write to:	Dissection Hotline Route 1, Box 541 Waynesville, NC 28786
Ask for:	• Saying No to Dissection handbook (grades K–6) • Objection to Dissection handbook (grades 7–12)

Reduce Litter

Litter is a widespread problem, but you can help make the world a cleaner place. This fact sheet provides information on how to get rid of the litter that pollutes our earth.

Directions:	Write your request on paper, and put it in an envelope. You must enclose a **long self-addressed, stamped envelope.**
Write to:	Keep America Beautiful Mill River Plaza 9 West Broad Street Stamford, CT 06902
Ask for:	Litter Tips fact sheet

KIND News for Kids

What do endangered animals, recycling, conservation, rock stars, sports figures, and kindness have in common? You'll find them all in *KIND News!* This classroom newspaper shows you how to be kind to animals, people, and the earth.

Directions:	Write your request on paper, and put it in an envelope. You must enclose 75¢ for **each** newspaper you request.
Write to:	KIND News Department FS P.O. Box 362 East Haddam, CT 06423-0362
Ask for:	• *KIND News Primary* (grades K–2) • *KIND News Junior* (grades 3–4) • *KIND News Senior* (grades 5–6)

Student Action Guide

Ever wonder what you can do to help save the environment? The *HSUS Student Action Guide* has lots of suggestions for forming your own earth and animal protection club. This fun newspaper from the Humane Society of the United States explains how to form a club, hold meetings, target issues, and plan activities.

Directions:	Write your name, address, and request on a postcard.
Write to:	HSUS Youth Education Division Department FS P.O. Box 362 East Haddam, CT 06423-0362
Ask for:	*HSUS Student Action Guide*

Greenpeace

Help Greenpeace preserve the earth and all the life it supports. These fact sheets will teach you more about the environment and what you can do to make a difference.

Directions:	Write your request on paper, and put it in an envelope. You must enclose a **long self-addressed, stamped envelope.**
Write to:	Greenpeace Public Information 1436 U Street NW Washington, DC 20009
Ask for:	• Atmosphere and Energy fact sheet • Tropical Forests fact sheet • Toxics Prevention fact sheet • Ocean Ecology fact sheet

Natural Energy

Learn how the ocean and the earth can be used to create energy. The Conservation and Renewable Energy Inquiry Referral Service (CAREIRS) has three fact sheets to send you about natural energy and energy conservation.

Directions:	Write your name, address, and request on a postcard.
Write to:	CAREIRS P.O. Box 8900 Silver Spring, MD 20907
Ask for:	• Energy Conservation—FS 218 • Ocean Energy—FS 221 • Geothermal Energy—FS 188

Learn to Conserve

Learn about conservation with these water and soil pamphlets. They'll explain flood damage and how to prevent it, how grass grows, how to practice soil and water conservation to the benefit of wildlife, and more!

Directions:	Write your request on paper, and put it in an envelope. You must enclose a **long self-addressed, stamped envelope** for **each** pamphlet you request.
Write to:	USDA Soil Conservation Service Room 0054–South P.O. Box 2890 Washington, DC 20013
Ask for:	• Flood Plain Management pamphlet • Going Wild with Soil and Water Conservation booklet • Mulches for Your Garden pamphlet

Wetlands Posters

These attractive and informative posters look great on your wall at home or in your school classroom. One has a terrific full-color photo of a wood duck. The other shows the earth's water cycles on one side and informative articles on the reverse side. *(Please specify which poster you want.)*

Directions:	Write your name, address, and request on a postcard.
Write to:	USDA Soil Conservation Service Room 0054–South P.O. Box 2890 Washington, DC 20013
Ask for:	• Wetlands and Wildlife poster • Conservation and Water Cycles poster *(Teachers—please order only one copy of each poster per classroom.)*

Rain Sticks

Make your own rain stick from recycled materials at home. A rain stick is a traditional percussion instrument made by the people of the Brazilian rain forest. Tip it over and you hear the magical sound of rain falling on leaves. You'll get **rain-stick instructions and a bookmark.**

Directions:	Write your request on paper, and put it in an envelope. You must enclose a **long self-addressed, stamped envelope** and **$1.00.**
Write to:	Tropical Rain Eco-Sticks 2915 Heidi Drive San Jose, CA 95132
Ask for:	Tropical Rain Eco-Stick instructions

Globe Key Chains

Have the world in your pocket! This set of earth key chains features colorful globes that are strong and hard to lose. You'll get two.

Directions:	Write your request on paper, and put it in an envelope. You must enclose **$1.00.**
Write to:	Lightning Enterprises P.O. Box 16121 West Palm Beach, FL 33416
Ask for:	Two globe key chains

MEADOWBROOK PRESS

1995 EDITION

U.S. MAIL

HOBBIES AND CRAFTS

Stamp Newsletter

Being a philatelist is fun! The Junior Philatelists of America is a club for kids who like to collect stamps. Send for their newsletter to learn all the latest information about this exciting hobby.

Directions:	Write your request on paper, and put it in an envelope. You must enclose a **long self-addressed, stamped envelope** and **$1.00.**
Write to:	Junior Philatelists of America P.O. Box 850–P Boalsburg, PA 16827-0850
Ask for:	Newsletter

Foreign Stamps

Foreign stamps make a terrific addition to any collection. Now you can get a packet of twenty canceled and uncanceled stamps from any of over 40 countries. At least five stamps in every packet will feature art from Disney animated films.

Directions:	Write your request on paper, and put it in an envelope. You must enclose a **long self-addressed, stamped envelope** and **$1.00** for **each** packet of stamps you request.
Write to:	Ellen Williams P.O. Box 070914 New York, NY 11207
Ask for:	Packet of twenty canceled and uncanceled foreign stamps

Collecting Coins

Coin collecting has been around since the seventh century B.C. Anyone can start a collection—all it takes is a little know-how. This fifteen-page booklet tells you how to start a collection and how to preserve your coins once you get them.

Directions:	Write your request on paper, and put it in an envelope. You must enclose a **long self-addressed, stamped envelope** with **two first-class stamps** on it.
Write to:	American Numismatic Association Membership Department—KS 818 North Cascade Avenue Colorado Springs, CO 80903
Ask for:	Coin Collecting booklet

Old and Foreign Coins

Here's a chance to start your coin collection! You can choose between an old Lincoln penny, made between 1909 and 1939, or a coin from a foreign country. You won't get the same coin if you order more than one.

Directions:	Write your request on paper, and put it in an envelope. You must enclose a **long self-addressed, stamped envelope** and **25¢** for **each** coin you request.
Write to:	DND Coins Department MP–3 P.O. Box 1356 Gwinn, MI 49841
Ask for:	• One old Lincoln penny • One foreign coin

Make "Play Clay"

Gloomy outside? It must be a "Play Clay" day! Have lots of fun with clay you make from baking soda and other common ingredients. This fold-out shows you how to make jewelry, ornaments, and more!

Directions:	Write your request on paper, and put it in an envelope. You must enclose a **long self-addressed, stamped envelope.**
Write to:	Play Clay Arm & Hammer Department FS95 P.O. Box 826 Spring House, PA 19477
Ask for:	How to Make Play Clay activity foldout

Seed Packets

Here's your chance to start a window garden and find out if you have a green thumb! You can choose from flowers or vegetables.

Directions:	Write your request on paper, and put it in an envelope. You must enclose a **long self-addressed, stamped envelope.** *(Additional packets are available for **25¢ each**.)*
Write to:	ACE Hardware Department MP–3 P.O. Box 630 Gwinn, MI 49841
Ask for:	• Packet of flower seeds • Packet of vegetable seeds

Craft Kits

If you like to work with a needle and thread, you'll enjoy this selection of craft kits. Choose from needlepoint, quickpoint, crewel, cross-stitch, or latch hook.

Directions:	Write your request on paper, and put it in an envelope. You must enclose **$1.00** for **each** kit you request.
Write to:	Surprise Gift-of-the-Month Club Department NC P.O. Box 1 Stony Point, NY 10980
Ask for:	Craft kit (please specify which type of kit you want)

Fun Idea Sheets

You can make cool toys from stuff around the house or try new crafts with these idea sheets.

Directions:	Write your request on paper, and put it in an envelope. You must enclose a **long self-addressed, stamped envelope** for **each** sheet you request.
Write to:	Children's Museum Shop 300 Congress Street Boston, MA 02210
Ask for:	• Balloon and Funnel Pump • Tin Can Pump • Making Large Bubbles • Special Bubble Machine • Pie Plate Water Wheel • Spinning Top That Writes • Building Blocks from Milk Cartons • Siphon Bottles • Explorations with Food Coloring • Stained Glass Cookies • Making Simple Books • Organdy Screening

Model Railroads

Building model railroads and trains is lots of fun—especially because you're making something that moves! This colorful, photo-filled booklet shows you what this unique hobby is all about.

Directions:	Write your name, address, and request on a postcard.
Write to:	Kalmbach Publishing 21207 Crossroads Circle Waukesha, WI 53187 ATTN: Marketing/Promotions Department
Ask for:	Your Introduction to Model Railroading booklet

Model Rockets

You can run your own miniature Cape Canaveral. Spacemodeling is the space-age hobby that's great for school projects, science fairs, or just for fun. This pamphlet will tell you more.

Directions:	Write your name, address, and request on a postcard.
Write to:	National Association of Rocketry P.O. Box 177 Altoona, WI 54720
Ask for:	Spacemodeling pamphlet

MEADOWBROOK PRESS 1995 EDITION

U.S. MAIL

HEALTH AND SAFETY

Cancer Comic Book

This colorful, action-packed comic book stars Spider-Man, Storm, and Power Man as they battle an all-new supervillain, Smokescreen. Read it, and see how smoking affects your life—for the worse.

Directions:	Write your name, address, and request on a postcard.
Write to:	Your local American Cancer Society office. It's listed in the telephone book.
Ask for:	Spider-Man cancer comic book

Dealing with Cancer

Your local branch of the American Cancer Society offers a variety of materials that will teach you about cancer prevention and coping with cancer. You may request one or all of the items.

Directions:	Write your name, address, and request on a postcard.
Write to:	Your local American Cancer Society office. It's listed in the telephone book.
Ask for:	• Starting Free storybook • What Happened to You Happened to Me booklet • Helping Children Understand: A Guide for a Parent with Cancer booklet • When Your Brother or Sister Has Cancer booklet

Learn about Your Lungs

The American Lung Association makes learning about your lungs fun. They offer a coloring book, a crossword-puzzle book, and an activity book. Specify which items you want.

Directions:	Write your name, address, and request on a postcard.
Write to:	American Lung Association GPO Box #596-RB New York, NY 10116-0596
Ask for:	• **#0840** No Smoking, Lungs at Work activity book • **#0043** No Smoking coloring book

No Smoking Sign

When you can't breathe, nothing else matters.® Tell your family and friends that you don't want them to smoke by hanging up this sign that warns: Lungs at Work, No Smoking.

Directions:	Write your name, address, and request on a postcard.
Write to:	American Lung Association GPO Box #596-RB New York, NY 10116-0596
Ask for:	**#0121** Lungs at Work sign

Learn about Braces

You can learn all about orthodontics and wearing braces from this newsletter and these two pamphlets. Please specify which items you want.

Directions:	Write your name, address, and request on a postcard.
Write to:	American Association of Orthodontists Department KD 401 North Lindbergh Boulevard Saint Louis, MO 63141-7816
Ask for:	• Smiles newsletter • Facts about Orthodontics pamphlet • Careers in Orthodontics pamphlet

Helping Each Other

This coloring book teaches you about four serious illnesses that sometimes affect kids and adults. You'll learn about diabetes, epilepsy, mental illness, and hypertension.

Directions:	Write your name, address, and request on a postcard.
Write to:	Sandoz 59 Route 10 East Hanover, NJ 07936 ATTN: Mature Market
Ask for:	Helping Each Other coloring book

Helping Grandma

Does someone you love have Alzheimer's disease? This coloring book shows you what happens when a person gets this disease and how loved ones can help him or her cope with it.

Directions:	Write your name, address, and request on a postcard.
Write to:	Sandoz 59 Route 10 East Hanover, NJ 07936 ATTN: Mature Market
Ask for:	Helping Grandma coloring book

Health Coloring Books

Taking care of your health and knowing what to do in an emergency are important. Here are three sixteen-page coloring and activity books that explain trips to the dentist, calling 911, and saying no to drugs. Please specify which books you want.

Directions:	Write your request on paper, and put it in an envelope. You must enclose **$1.00** and **two first-class stamps** for **each** coloring book you request.
Write to:	Safe Child P.O. Box 40 1594 Brooklyn, NY 11240-1594
Ask for:	• In an Emergency Dial 911 coloring book • My Friend the Dentist coloring book • Winning Kids Don't Need Drugs coloring book

Heart-Shaped Bandages

The next time you get a scrape or cut and need a bandage, try these colorful heart-shaped bandages. They'll put a smile on your face as they protect your wound so it can heal. You'll get six.

Directions:	Write your request on paper, and put it in an envelope. You must enclose a **long self-addressed, stamped envelope** and **$1.00.**
Write to:	Stickers 'N' Stuff Department RB6 P.O. Box 430 Louisville, CO 80027
Ask for:	Six heart-shaped bandages

Special Olympics

Special Olympics celebrates the athletic achievements of people with mental retardation. Their free materials tell you how this special program works and how you can get involved as a volunteer.

Join the World of Winners

Directions:	Write your name, address, and request on a postcard.
Write to:	Special Olympics International c/o Free Stuff for Kids 1350 New York Avenue NW Suite 500 Washington, DC 20005
Ask for:	Free information for kids

Learn about Stuttering

Stuttering is a speech problem that affects 25 percent of kids at one time or another. You may want to talk for a person who stutters, but you shouldn't. You should try to be patient and take turns talking. Learn more about stuttering from these pamphlets.

STUTTERING
FOUNDATION OF
AMERICA

Directions:	Write your name, address, and request on a postcard or call 1-800-992-9392.
Write to:	Stuttering Foundation P.O. Box 11749 Memphis, TN 38111-0749
Ask for:	• If You Think Your Child Is Stuttering pamphlet • The Child Who Stutters at School: Notes to the Teacher pamphlet • Did You Know fact sheet • How to React When Speaking With Someone Who Stutters fact sheet

UNICEF Materials

Send for the famous UNICEF (United Nations Children's Fund) orange collection carton so you can collect donations for UNICEF this Halloween. You'll also get a Halloween safety tips bookmark.

Directions:	Write your request on paper, and put it in an envelope. You must enclose an **8-by-10-inch self-addressed, stamped envelope** with **two first-class stamps** on it.
Write to:	U.S. Committee for UNICEF Group Programs Department 2044P 333 East 38th Street New York, NY 10016
Ask for:	Trick-or-treat for UNICEF collection carton and safety tips bookmark

Join SADD

SADD (Students Against Driving Drunk) works to end death and injury on the highways due to drinking and driving. You will receive a "Contract for Life" which your parents and you can discuss and sign. You'll also get a SADD bumper sticker.

Directions:	Write your request on paper, and put it in an envelope. You must enclose a **long self-addressed, stamped envelope** and **$1.00**.
Write to:	SADD P.O. Box 800 Marlboro, MA 01752
Ask for:	SADD Contract for Life and bumper sticker

Kinderprint Kit

Staying safe is important. This Kinderprint kit is a good way to keep a record of all your physical characteristics for easy identification, just in case you get hurt or lost. The file contains a place for your photo, helpful safety tips, a fingerprint kit, and a balloon.

Directions:	Write your request on paper, and put it in an envelope. You must enclose a **long self-addressed, stamped envelope** and **$1.00.**
Write to:	Special Products Department FS 34 Romeyn Avenue Amsterdam, NY 12010
Ask for:	Kinderprint kit

Operation Lifesaver

Operation Lifesaver wants you to stay safe and sound. Their coloring and activity book will show you how to keep out of danger around railroad tracks. You can also get a bookmark that reminds you to "Look, Listen ... and Live."

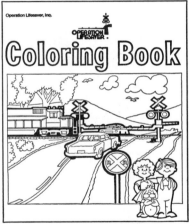

Directions:	Write your name, address, and request on a postcard.
Write to:	Operation Lifesaver 1420 King Street, Suite 401 Alexandria, VA 22314
Ask for:	• Coloring/activity book • Bookmark *(Limit **one** item per request.)*

Bike Safety

This coloring book teaches you about bike safety and why it's so important. You'll learn everything from hand signals to how to check your bike for safety before you ride.

Directions:	Write your name, address, and request on a postcard.
Write to:	Triaminic Sandoz 59 Route 10 East Hanover, NJ 07936
Ask for:	Helping with Bike Safety coloring book

Be a Safe Biker

Now you can learn how to take good care of your bicycle and how to ride it safely. Pick up these and other safety tips and health habits from this pamphlet and these two coloring books. Please specify which items you want.

Directions:	For the pamphlet, write your request on paper, and put it in an envelope. You must enclose a **long self-addressed, stamped envelope.** For the coloring books, write your full name and address on a postcard.
Write to:	Aetna Life & Casualty Public Service Library RE6H 151 Farmington Avenue Hartford, CT 06156
Ask for:	• Safe Biking pamphlet • Just Ask coloring book • Play It Safe coloring book

INDEX

INDEX

A Bad Case of the Giggles

selected by Bruce Lansky

Get out of earshot and bolt the doors when you discover this book . . . it will leave you with "a bad case of the giggles." It's jam-packed with poems about stinky feet, burps, greasy grimy gopher guts, and other topics kids find hilarious. The book contains poems by favorite poets: Shel Silverstein, Jack Prelutsky, Judith Viorst, and Jeff Moss. To top it all off, the book contains 100 zany illustrations by Stephen Carpenter. Lansky and Carpenter have successfully collaborated on *Kids Pick the Funniest Poems* and *The New Adventures of Mother Goose.*

Order #2411

Order Form

Quantity	Title	Author	Order No.	Unit Cost	Total
	A Bad Case of the Giggles	Lansky, Bruce	2411	$14.00	
	Dads Say the Dumbest Things!	Lansky/Jones	4220	$6.00	
	Dino Dots	Dixon, Dougal	2250	$4.95	
	Free Stuff for Kids	Free Stuff Editors	2190	$5.00	
	Hocus Pocus Stir & Cook, Kitchen Science	Lewis, James	2380	$7.00	
	How To Embarrass Your Kids	Holleman/Sherins	4005	$6.00	
	Kids' Holiday Fun	Warner, Penny	6000	$12.00	
	Kids' Party Games and Activities	Warner, Penny	6095	$12.00	
	Kids Pick the Funniest Poems	Lansky, Bruce	2410	$14.00	
	Learn While You Scrub, Science in the Tub	Lewis, James	2350	$7.00	
	Moms Say the Funniest Things!	Lansky, Bruce	4280	$6.00	
	New Adventures of Mother Goose	Lansky, Bruce	2420	$15.00	
	Webster's Dictionary Game	Webster, Wilbur	6030	$5.95	
	Weird Wonders and Bizarre Blunders	Schreiber, Brad	4120	$4.95	
				Subtotal	
			Shipping and Handling (see below)		
			MN residents add 6.5% sales tax		
				Total	

YES, please send me the books indicated above. Add $2.00 shipping and handling for the first book and $.50 for each additional book. Add $2.50 to total for books shipped to Canada. Overseas postage will be billed. Allow up to 4 weeks for delivery. Send check or money order payable to Meadowbrook Press. No cash or C.O.D.'s, please. Prices subject to change without notice. **Quantity discounts available upon request.**

Send book(s) to:

Name _____ Phone _____

Address _____

City _____ State _____ Zip_____

Payment via:

❑ Check or money order payable to Meadowbrook Press. (No cash or C.O.D.'s, please.) Amount enclosed $_____

❑ Visa (for orders over $10.00 only)   ❑ MasterCard (for orders over $10.00 only)

Account # _____ Signature _____ Exp. Date _____

A *FREE* Meadowbrook Press catalog is available upon request.

You can also phone us for orders of $10.00 or more at 1-800-338-2232.

Mail to: Meadowbrook, Inc., 18318 Minnetonka Blvd., Deephaven, MN 55391

Toll-Free 1-800-338-2232

(612) 473-5400   FAX (612) 475-0736